GOAL!

Level 4 Workbook

Accompanies the Level 4 Goal! reading books:

From Africa ... to Wembley

A Very Odd Sort of Job

How to be a Star Keeper

How to be a Star in Midfield

Dark Star Part one

Dark Star Part two

Dark Star Part three

Dark Star Part four

By Nicola Pointon

Ransom

Level 4 Workbook
by Nicola Pointon

Photographs by Joe Pepler
Illustrated by Diego Jourdan & Mauro Serafini

Published by Ransom Publishing Ltd.
51 Southgate Street, Winchester, Hants. SO23 9EH, UK
www.ransom.co.uk

ISBN 978 184167 887 0
First published in 2008
Copyright © 2008 Ransom Publishing Ltd.
Illustrations copyright © 2008 Diego Jourdan & Mauro Serafini
Photographs copyright © 2008 Portsmouth Football Club

A CIP catalogue record of this book is available from the British Library.
The rights of Nicola Pointon to be identified as the author and of Diego Jourdan & Mauro Serafini to be
identified as the illustrators of this Work have been asserted by them in accordance with sections 77 and
78 of the Copyright, Design and Patents Act 1988.

Printed in the United Kingdom by HSW Print.
Thanks to everyone at Portsmouth F.C. who gave invaluable help in developing this series.

Contents

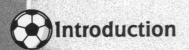

1 Introduction

This workbook accompanies *Goal!*, a football-themed early reading series especially designed for older students who have never got to grips with conventional reading schemes. Using a synthetic phonics approach, the series progresses over five levels, broadly following the UK government's *Letters and Sounds* programme.

As a high interest series, *Goal!* adopts a more flexible approach than a fully decodable programme, taking into account the higher level experiental oral skills of the students and featuring football-orien-tated vocabulary which makes the books truly engaging and, above all, readable.

This workbook covers eight books at Level 4 of *Goal!* (corresponding to Phase 4 of *Letters and Sounds*). The books covered are:

From Africa ... to Wembley	**Dark Star Part one**
A Very Odd Sort of Job	**Dark Star Part two**
How to be a Star Keeper	**Dark Star Part three**
How to be a Star in Midfield	**Dark Star Part four**

With the older student in mind, this workbook offers a combination of open-ended interactive games, as well as the more traditional-style worksheets. The resources are:

 linked to the content of the reading books;

 designed to support the learning objectives at their specific level;

 highly visual, engaging and fun; and

 age appropriate, suitably challenging and achievable.

Note: in this workbook the terms *student* and *child* are used interchangeably. Apologies if it sometimes feels inappropriate.

2 Teacher's Notes for Worksheets

Worksheet One: African Soccer Stars (From Africa … to Wembley)

Task: To work towards researching information independently and to communicate the new-found knowledge.

Activity: Use a globe, an atlas or a map of the world (Google Earth or similar would be ideal, if accessible) to help the children locate the continent of Africa and relate it back to where they live.

Ask the children to find the country in Africa where John Utaka comes from (Nigeria). This offers an opportunity to identify many other African countries. These could be labelled on the map on the worksheet.

Introduce the worksheet and explain that the children must now find out about some other players (up to a maximum of five) that have come from an African country. For each player the children should write in the player's name, their age, the country they were born and the position they play. There is also space on the worksheet for the children to write in some additional information about the player, to draw a picture of the player, or to draw the national flag of the player's country.

The children may have their own choices of player to research, but suggested players are:

Didier Drogba (Ivory Coast)
Samuel Eto'o (Cameroon)
Kanu (Nigeria)
Benjani Mwaruwari (Zimbabwe)

Papa Bouba Diop (Senegal)
Ahmed Hossan (Mido) (Egypt)
Aaron Mokoena (South Africa)
Emmanuel Adebayor (Togo)
Frederic Kanoute (Mali) and
Sulley Muntari (Ghana).

Once complete, ask the children to share their findings with the group.

Worksheet Two: Read the World (From Africa … to Wembley)

Task: This activity focuses on helping to create a positive attitude towards reading.

Activity: Look at and discuss the places around the world where John Utaka has played football for professional clubs. (He started in Nigeria, then moved to Cairo in Egypt, Qatar, Rennes in France and then Portsmouth in the UK.) Then focus on John's passion for reading.

Take the opportunity to discuss the children's reading patterns, their likes and dislikes and their general feelings about reading.

Then ask the children to read the left-hand page of the notebook, where John Utaka has answered some questions about reading. Ask the children to fill in the right-hand side of the book, answering similar questions about their own reading habits. Use John Utaka's example to help them.

Worksheet Three: Not Just a Footballer (A Very Odd Sort of Job)

Task: Writing simple phrases to explain thoughts and feelings about future career paths.

Activity: Ask the children for their thoughts about the job of a professional footballer. Explain that even the most successful footballers often had to begin by doing other jobs. In addition, a footballer's playing career does not last for very long, so most players will need another job afterwards.

Ask the children to read through the fascinating range of current or former occupations undertaken by the footballers named on the worksheet. Ask the children if they can think of any other careers that footballers could do when they finish their playing career.

Next ask children to think about the job they would like to do and why they would like to do it.

Ask them to draw themselves in their chosen profession and then write some short phrases (in the text boxes next to the illustration) to explain their choice.

Worksheet Four: One day I want to play for … (A Very Odd Sort of Job)

Task: Developing research skills and using the information gathered to create a piece of writing. There is also opportunity to write a more reflective piece of writing.

Activity: Ask the children which club, if they had the chance, they would like to play for.

Encourage lots of open and exciting discussion, especially getting the children to justify their opinions and give detailed explanations.

Then ask the children to complete the worksheet, using the Internet or library resources to find the factual club information required.

Remind them about their thoughts and feelings (that they have already spoken about) and how this will help them to complete their writing.

Worksheet Five: Keeper's Bloomers (How to be a Star Keeper)

Task: Recalling the advice from the book and being able to use this information to write some tips for goalkeepers.

Activity: Ask the children to look at the photographs at the top of the worksheet and to discuss how an error by a goalkeeper can often – if not usually – result in a goal for the opposition. Ask the children to suggest the type of errors they might have seen a goalkeeper make (e.g. mis-judging a ball and not catching it, standing in the wrong place, punching a ball they should have caught, etc.).

Now focus on both the coach and the keeper and ask the children to write on the worksheet the type of advice a coach might give a goalkeeper to improve his game. The ideas will need to be expressed in a way that is short, clear and easy to remember. Encourage the children to pursue their own ideas as well as those suggested by Gary Stevens.

Finally, once the activity is completed, give the children a chance to share their ideas with the rest of the group.

Worksheet Six: Swap Shop (How to be a Star Keeper)

Task: To expand the vocabulary and look for synonyms.

Activity: Explain to (or remind) the children what a synonym is. Give the children some examples, and explain that sometimes choosing a different word (with a similar meaning) can make the sentence more meaningful.

Show the children the worksheet and ask them to read each sentence through carefully.

Direct children to look at the word in each sentence that is underlined and in bold. Ask them to think of a similar word or synonym that they could use that would not affect the context of the sentence and indeed might improve it. They should then write out the full sentence underneath, using their new word.

Encourage the children to share their words within their group and discuss which words were most successful in keeping the sentence very much the same or in improving the sentence.

Worksheet Seven: Midfield Magic (How to be a Star in Midfield)

Task: To consolidate knowledge of rhyming final consonant blends and text recall.

Activity: Ask children to think of words that can be used to describe a pass in football (e.g. cross, chip, volley) and to write them in the eight footballs at the top of the sheet.

Now explain that they must try and think of another word that rhymes with each one that has been written in a football (e.g. cross – toss, chip – trip, etc.).

Finally, at the bottom of the worksheet ask the children to write a short passage, in their own words, describing the job of a midfield football player.

Worksheet Eight: Boss the Ball (How to be a Star in Midfield)

Task: To write simple explanatory text and use simple diagrams to aid their explanations.

Activity: Ask the children to tell you about any football skills they can do or that they have seen

a player do. If possible, let them demonstrate using a football!

Then encourage the children to choose up to three skills they know/can do and draw a simple diagram on their sheet to explain each trick. They should accompany each diagram with some simple written explanations.

When completed, the children could swap worksheets and then, with a football, each child could follow the diagrams & explanations to attempt the trick.

Worksheet Nine: Dark Star – The Play (Dark Star Part one)

Task: Being able to undertake a role within a story (i.e. a play).

Activity: (This activity covers four worksheets.) The activity ideally requires a group of four children to work together but can be undertaken with a smaller or larger number.

There are four characters in *Dark Star Part one: The Start*. These are: Art, Janaki, Scooter and Zardoz. Select one child from the group to act as each character. Photocopy the character cut-outs from the worksheets (four pages) onto stiff card, or glue them onto card, as appropriate. Fold the tabs back so the characters stand up.

The four children will be required to act out the story *Dark Star Part one: The Start*, so they will need to discuss how to play each character. Recap the story, identifying the key points, and discuss how each of the characters would be feeling at each point in the story. Encourage the children to make up a voice for each character and even use some props, if available.

Give the children plenty of opportunity to plan, rehearse and practice prior to a performance. If possible, encourage the group to perform their play to the rest of their class or year group.

Teacher's Notes for Worksheets

Worksheet Ten: Spaceship SOS! (Dark Star Part one)

Task: To recall the story and to write imaginatively and empathetically.

Activity: First ask the children to recall the story of Dark Star Part one, highlighting the key parts of the plot. Make it clear that at the end of the book there are many questions left unanswered, such as who are the three characters on the spaceship, why are they on a spaceship in the first place (and how did they get there), to whom does the spaceship belong, who is Zardoz and what does he want of them, etc.

Then guide the children back to the last moment of the story, when Zardoz tells them that the spaceship is about to land on his planet. Show the children the worksheet and the blank computer screen, complete with an empty email window ready to send a message back to Earth. Ask the children to think about a message they could send to summon help. What would they say in this message?

Once discussed, children can write their plea for help, ready to be sent back to Earth!

Worksheet Eleven: Are you a Dark Star Expert? (Dark Star Part two)

Task: This activity focuses on reading for meaning and writing simple sentences.

Activity: Remind the children of the story and direct them to look at the key pictures and characters in the book as you do so.

Then ask the children to look at the worksheet. Work through the questions together and encourage the children to verbalise a simple answer to each question. Then ask them to write the answer as a simple sentence. Show how to use the words from the question to help form the answer.

Worksheet Twelve: Star Words (Dark Star Part two)

Task: Using adjectives to describe characters and using adjectives successfully in simple sentences.

Activity: Ask the children to look at each of the characters on the worksheet in turn and think of and suggest appropriate words that could be used to describe them, based upon what they haved learned from the characters in the book.

Now ask the children to write these words in the bubbles surrounding each character, remembering to say the words to themselves first, segment the word and listen to the blends and sounds they hear.

Finally, ask the children to write a short sentence about each character at the bottom of the worksheet. They should include one or more of the adjectives they have already chosen for each character.

Extension: The character who works for Zardoz and talks to him on the 'videophone' device has no name in the book. Based upon his character, can the children think of a suitable name for him?

Worksheet Thirteen: All Mixed Up! (Dark Star Part three)

Task: Word ordering and sentence building.

Activity: Explain to the children that the worksheet contains a number of mixed-up sentences taken from the story. The sentences need to be unmixed so that they make sense.

First read the mixed up sentences together and then ask children to reorder the words so that the sentence makes sense. Remind the children that there are two clues to help them find the first and last words in a sentence: first, a sentence always begins with a capital letter, and second, a sentence always ends with a full stop.

Ask the children to write out the sentences correctly and to check their own work once they think they have finished.

The completed sentences are:

1. The rocket lands with a bump.

2. The screen flickers on and Zardoz appears with a sinister grin.

3. What is waiting for them outside?

4. They are sure something bad is going to happen

5. They are taken to a football pitch.

6. Oh yes, they are top class.

Worksheet Fourteen: Cosmic Connectives (Dark Star Part three)

Task: Reading and writing longer sentences and using connectives in writing sentences.

Activity: Look at the worksheet with the children. Explain that it contains a number of unfinished sentences. Point out that the last word in each sentence is in bold: introduce the term connective if appropriate and then highlight these connectives that are written in bold. Explain the function of a connective.

Then ask the children to complete these unfinished sentences. If they wish they can attempt to finish the sentences using the information they can glean from the story. Alternatively, they could use their imagination to include in their sentences something that is not apparent from the text (e.g. the Dark Star looked gloomy because smoke from factories or volcanoes filled the skies).

When they have finished, ask them to share their work with each other, taking it in turns to read one sentence at a time.

Worksheet Fifteen: The Bad Guys (Dark Star Part four)

Task: To write a short conversation between two characters; beginning to recognise that spoken text is much less formal than written text.

Activity: Reflect with the children on the story developments in the final part of Dark Star. Note that Zardoz gets to lose the cup – by virtue of a trick. Discuss how he is likely to feel. What is his response likely to be, based upon the children's experience of his behaviour in the story. It is likely that he will be angry and he will seek to blame somebody else. Then discuss how the coach for Zardoz's team is likely to feel. He has been ruthless too, but he has worked hard. Is Zardoz likely to blame him? What is his response likely to be? Will he accept criticism, or will he attempt to justify himself?

Can the children imagine the conversation the two characters would have had following the realisation that, not only had they lost the Cup Final, but also that the earthlings had run away.

Explain to the children that they are required to write a dialogue, or conversation, between these two characters after the game. Look again at the book, but this time focusing on the way in which speech is depicted – in the speech bubbles. Ask the children to compare the way speech is written with the sentences in the book. They are much less formal.

Encourage the children to think of possible pathways for the conversation. Once children have discussed and formalised a number of ideas, ask them to write their imaginary conversation between the two characters.

If the children are particularly enthused, they could even act it out!

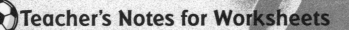

Worksheet Sixteen: You Can Tell the Story (Dark Star Part four)

Task: To sequence and label story cards accurately to tell a story.

Activity: The key illustrations from the four *Dark Star* books are contained on four worksheet pages. Each illustration is accompanied by a small box for the children to write in some simple text.

Photocopy and then cut out the story cards, and present them to the children in a random order. Ask the children to sequence the whole of the *Dark Star* story by placing the story cards in the correct order. Except for the first and last cards, all the story cards are arrow-shaped, so they can slot together to form a story sequence.

When the story is sequenced correctly the children can write some short text to accompany each illustration. They could then use the text notes and illustration sequence to tell the story out loud to the group.

This is an activity that could be printed and laminated so that children can write on the cards using a dry wipe pen and the activity can be used time and again.

Extension: The story could be extended (either in the middle or at the end) by deciding on new developments/locations and making new drawings to illustrate these developments. These could then be slotted into the story card sequence as appropriate.

Name:
Country:
Age:
Position:

Name:
Country:
Age:
Position:

Name some African soccer stars!

Name:
Country:
Age:
Position:

Name:
Country:
Age:
Position:

Name:
Country:
Age:
Position:

GOAL!

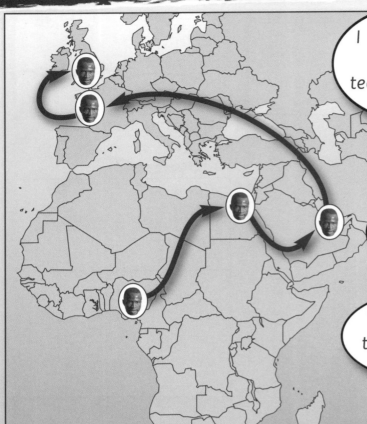

I have played for many teams in many places.

When I travel, I love to read.

When I finish training, I love to read.

When I'm in the bath, I love to read!

Favourite place to read:
   In bed before I sleep.

What do I like reading:
   Plays by Shakespeare.

Best book/paper/magazine:
   Hamlet

Why?:
   Because I love the plot.

Other people I know who love books:
   Team-mates David James and Richard Hughes.

How often do you read?:
   Every day!

Not Just a Footballer

GOAL!

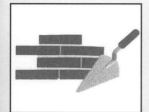	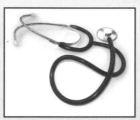			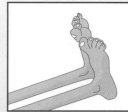
Dean Windass Hull City former builder	Arjan de Zeeuw ex-Portsmouth doctor	Stuart Pearce ex-England qualified electrician	Chris Waddle ex-England ex-sausage factory	Norman Whiteside ex-Man. Utd podiatrist

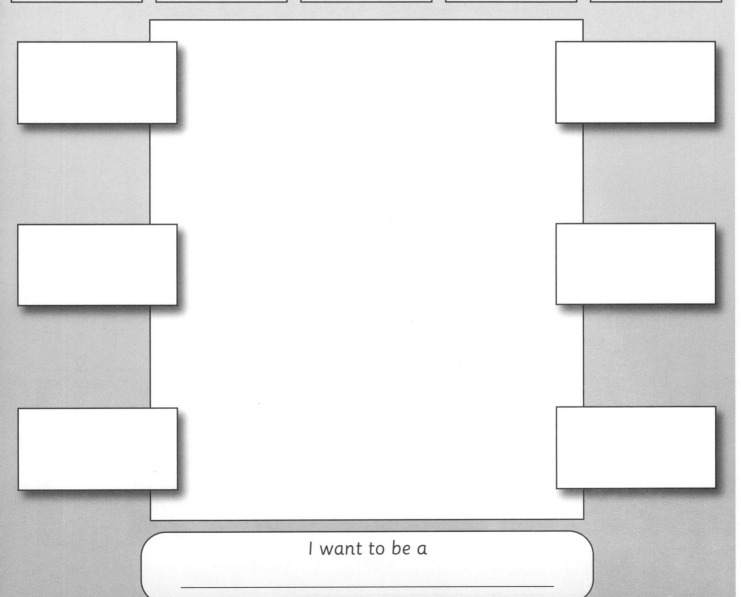

I want to be a

_____

One day I want to play for ...

GOAL!

One day I want to play for ...

Club:

Home venue:

League the club plays in:

Current manager:

Star players:

Club badge:

Why I want to play for

_____

Club colours:

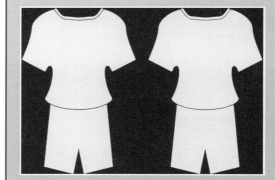

GOAL!

> Being a goalkeeper is hard. Most mistakes end up with a goal being scored.

> What are the top tips this coach is giving to his keeper?

GOAL!

Can you think of a better word?

Want to be a **top** keeper? Let's go.

_____

Look at the hands. They are **strong**.

_____

You may need to jump **high**.

_____

Is it safe to **catch** the ball?

_____

Touch the ball over the bar.

_____

Push it **past** the post.

_____

GOAL!

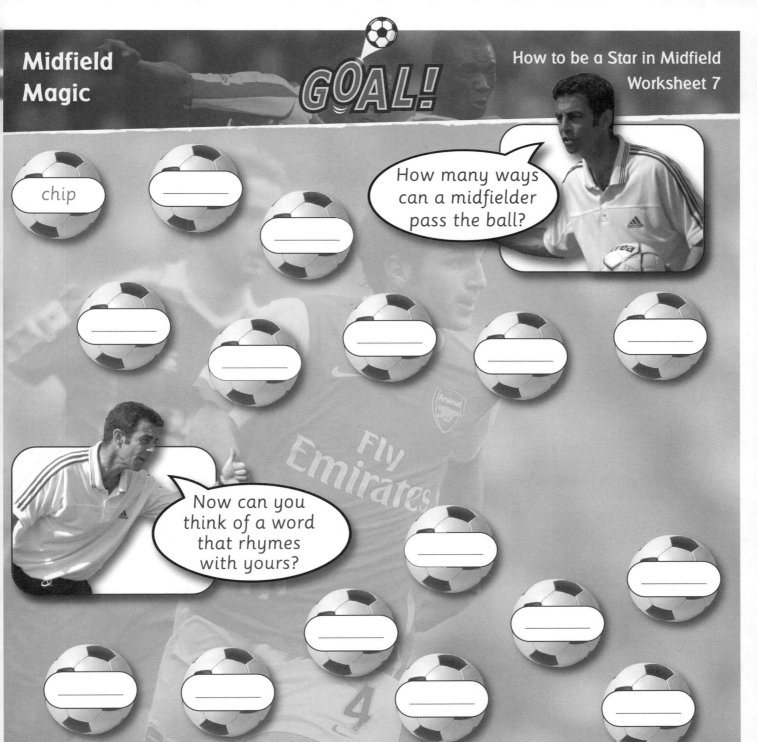

chip

How many ways can a midfielder pass the ball?

Now can you think of a word that rhymes with yours?

The job of a midfielder is to

Boss the Ball

GOAL!

How many flicks and tricks do you know?

Remember! To be a good midfielder you need to boss the ball.

GOAL!

GOAL!

GOAL!

GOAL!

GOAL!

Sender: _____

To: _____

_____

_____

_____

_____

_____

_____

_____

_____

_____

_____

_____

What does Dark Star look like?

_____

_____

What happens as they walk down the ramp?

_____

_____

Where are Janaki, Art and Scooter taken?

_____

_____

What 3 skills do they each show?

_____

_____

Where does Zardoz put the team?

_____

_____

What do you think Zardoz has planned for them?

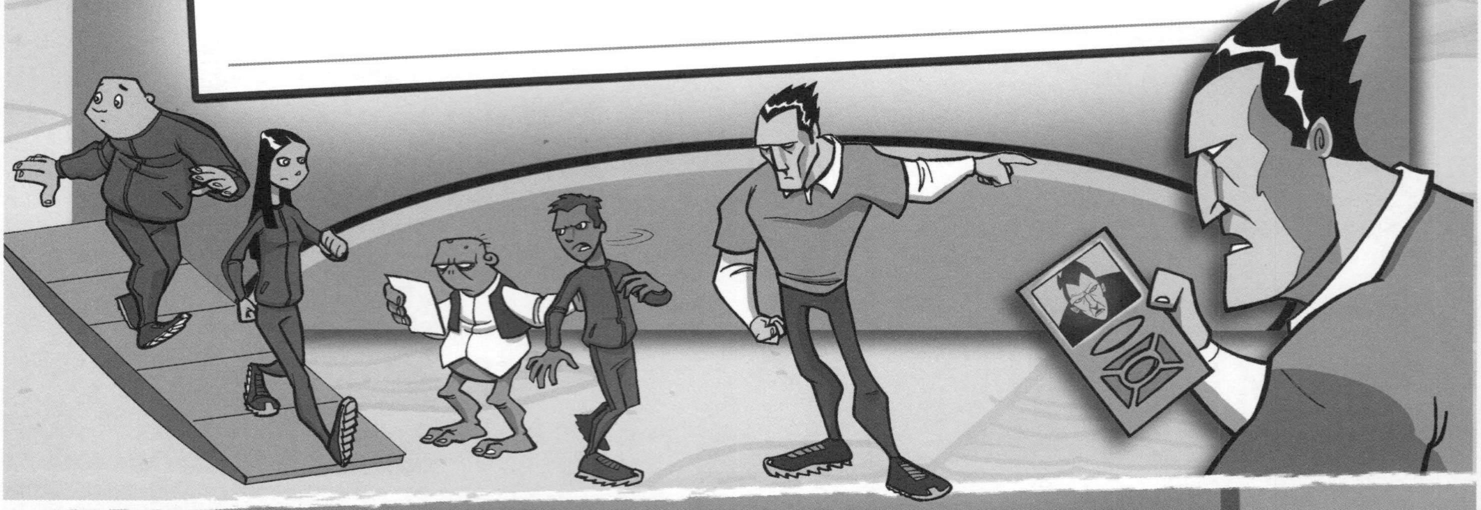

_____

_____

GOAL!

 _____

 _____

 _____

 _____

 _____

25

GOAL!

bump. The lands rocket a with

_____

Zardoz appears The on sinister with a grin. flickers and screen

_____

outside? What for waiting is them

_____

sure bad something They are happen. going to is

_____

taken are to They pitch. football a

_____

are they Oh class. yes, top

_____

GOAL!

These sentences are not finished. You **must** finish them ... **or else!**

The Dark Star planet looked gloomy **because** _____

_____

Zardoz showed them the exit **so** _____

_____

They left the rocket **but** _____

_____

They felt better **when** _____

_____

Art is a winger **and** _____

_____

Janaki pushed the ball over the bar **which** _____

_____

Dark Star might be champions **if** _____

_____

They were locked up **until** _____

_____

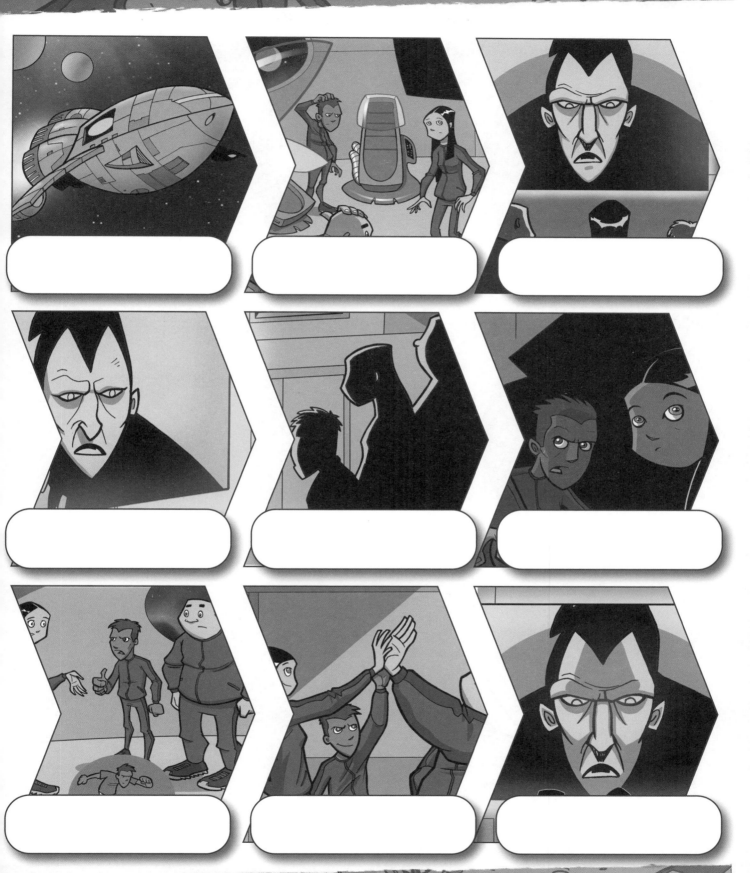

29

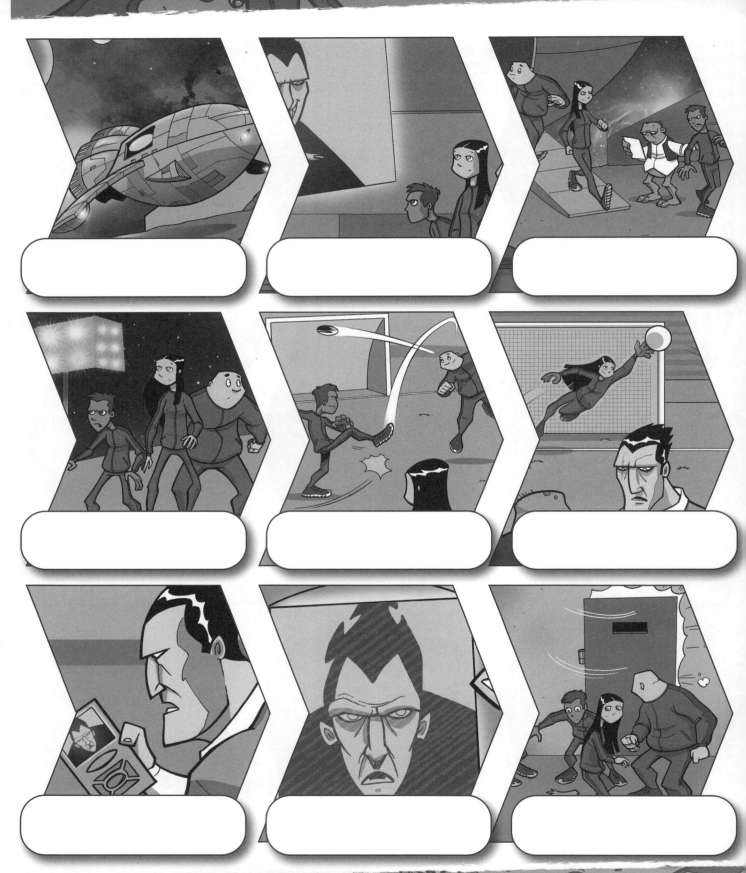

You Can Tell the Story

GOAL!

4 Teacher's Notes for Games and Activities

Super League Dominoes

The Game: A domino-style game which encourages students to build words, using the vocabulary encountered in the reading books.

Preparation: The game comprises three photocopiable sheets containing the domino cards. Photocopy the resources and cut them out.

How to Play: This game can be played by a student working alone, or together with an adult or support assistant, or the game can be played in small groups.

Each domino card is divided in half. Each half contains the start of a word (right-hand side) or the end of a word (on the left-hand side).

The student(s) must use all of the cards up by linking the cards together to form a series of words.

By lining the cards up at a slight angle, to make a large circle, the first and last cards can also be linked up, making a final word.

The words to make up are:

team	sort	manager
important	together	England
goalposts	pitch	different
premier	fantastic	understand
player	strong	catch
punch	wicked	practise
midfield	straight	rocket

winger	orders	darkness
sinister	floodlights	problem
champion	galaxy	robots.

Shootout on the Dark Star

The Game: A word recognition game for small groups of children.

Preparation: The game comprises six photocopiable sheets containing eight game boards, a letter spinner and a sheet of counters. Photocopy the resources and cut them out (photocopy as many of the game counters – Sheet 6 – as necessary). You will need a split pin or similar to make the spinner.

How to Play: One person needs to be the caller. This could be an adult/teacher or it could be a child. The caller has the spinner.

Give each child (except the caller) a game board and some counters. If there are more than eight children, they could work in groups. The caller then spins the arrow and calls out (not shows) the word selected. If the children have that word on their board, they cover it with a counter.

When all words on a board are covered that child shouts 'Zardoz sucks!'. They are the winner.

Soccer Sentences

The Game: A simple sentence building game for two or more players.

Preparation: The game comprises five photocopiable sheets containing a game board (Sheets 1 and 2) and three sheets of game counters. Photocopy the resources and cut them out. Using sticky tape or similar, stick the two parts of the game board together to make a playing board 12 squares wide and seven squares high. Mount the playing board on card as desired. If playing with a larger group of children (five or more players) you may prefer to copy and cut out a second set of game counters.

How to Play: Place all the game counters face down in the centre of the table. Each player picks up seven counters at random. Then, in turn, each player must use as many of their counters as possible to make a sentence. (The sentence must make grammatical sense, but it can be sensible or silly.) They then place the counters on the board to make the sentence.

The next player uses their counters to make another sentence, which they in turn place on the board. If they wish, they can make use of any of the words already on the board, by running their sentence vertically or horizontally around that word (similar to the way a crossword puzzle works).

The counters with the symbol ☺ on them can be used to denote any word of the player's choosing.

If a player is unable to make a word, they must pick up a counter from the table. Counters cannot be placed on the four squares containing football photographs.

The first player to use all their counters is the winner. If all the counters have been taken by players, but nobody can complete a sentence, the player with the lowest number of counters is the winner.

GOAL!

bots	te	am	so
rt	man	ager	import
ant	to	gether	Eng
land	goal	posts	pi
tch	diff	erent	Prem

GOAL!

 ier  fan

 tastic  under

 stand  play

 er  stro

 ng  ca

 tch  pun

 ch  wick

 ed  prac

 tise  mid

 field  stra

ight | **rock**

et | **wing**

er | **ord**

ers | **dark**

ness | **sin**

ister | **flood**

lights | **prob**

lem | **champ**

ion | **gal**

axy | **ro**

Sheet 3   **37**

GOAL!

Team Name: _____

Janaki   afraid   shocked

amazing   gloomy   sinister   flicker

Team Name: _____

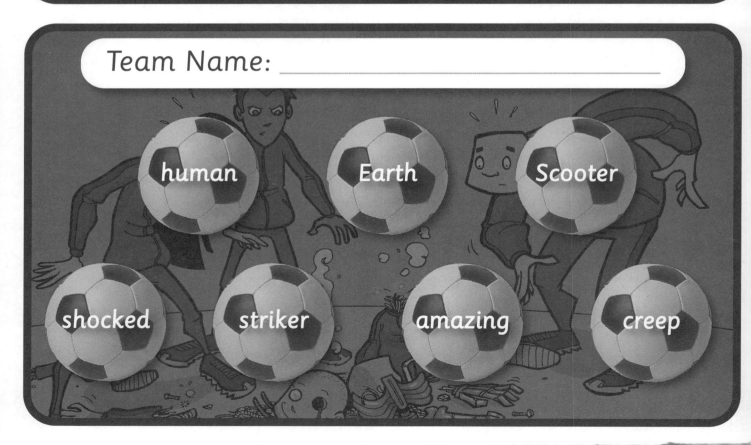

human   Earth   Scooter

shocked   striker   amazing   creep

GOAL!

Team Name: _____

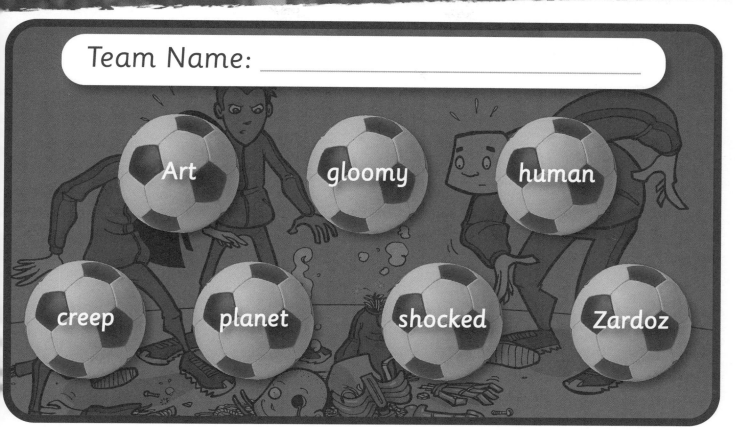

Art · gloomy · human
creep · planet · shocked · Zardoz

Team Name: _____

Art · human · amazing
blinding · champion · Janaki · problem

GOAL!

Team Name: _____

striker — creep — Scooter
Zardoz — sinister — afraid — champion

Team Name: _____

Zardoz — flicker — striker
Art — blinding — planet — Scooter

Team Name: _____

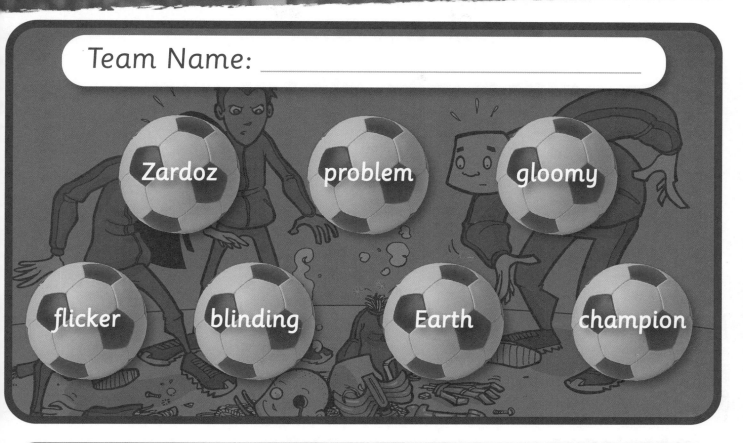

Zardoz problem gloomy

flicker blinding Earth champion

Team Name: _____

Earth problem afraid

human planet Janaki sinister

GOAL!

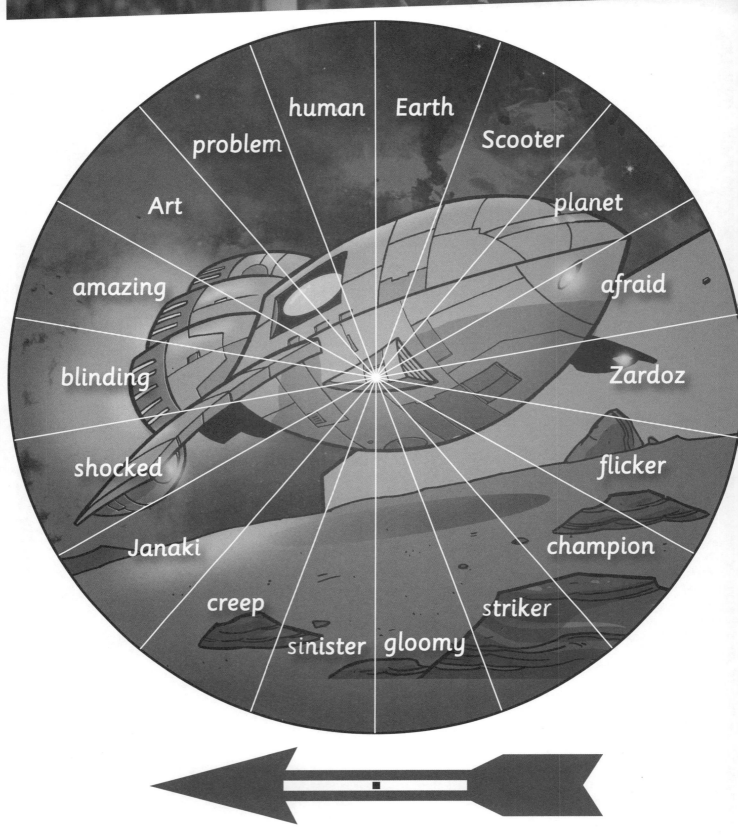

43

Soccer Sentences

GOAL!

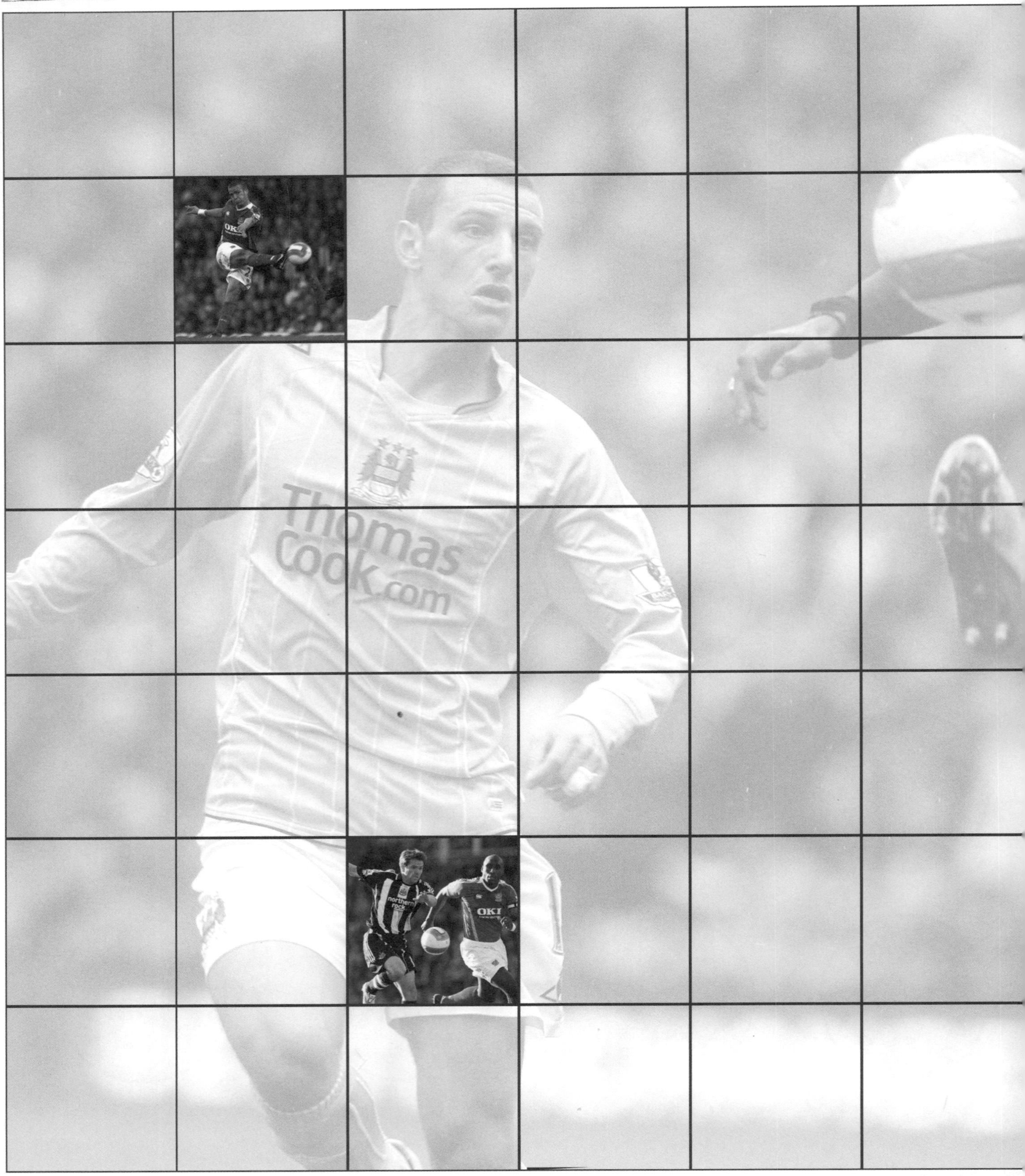

GOAL!

 in

 is

 am

 I

 star

 a

 midfield

 the

 ball

 player

 he

 cool

 wicked

 skills

 have

 can

GOAL!

 pass

 has

 well

 game

 control

 keeper

 top

 win

 must

 dive

 this

 punch

 away

 save

 great

 score

 stay

 beat

 for

 shoot

 hit

 bend

 defender

 tackle

 clear

 striker